THE FANTASTICALLY FUNNY JOKE BOOK

ARCTURUS

ARCTURUS

This edition published in 2016 by Arcturus Publishing Limited
26/27 Bickels Yard, 151–153 Bermondsey Street,
London SE1 3HA

ISBN: 978-1-78599-307-7
CH004984NT
Supplier 29, Date 0516, Print run 4998

Written by Lisa Regan
Designed by Trudi Webb
Edited by Rebecca Clunes
Illustrations from Shutterstock

Printed in China

CONTENTS

WHAT DO YOU GET IF YOU CROSS T-REX AND AN EVIL WITCH?

I DON'T KNOW, BUT I'D DEFINITELY RUN AWAY FROM IT!

DIVE IN HEADFIRST TO FIND HUNDREDS MORE LAUGHS LIKE THIS. THE SIX SENSATIONAL, SNIGGER-TASTIC SECTIONS ARE PACKED FULL OF CHUCKLES AND GROANS TO SHARE WITH YOUR LOVED ONES, OR TO KEEP YOU GIGGLING TO YOURSELF AT NIGHT.

SO, NEXT TIME YOUR FRIENDS ALL MOAN THAT THERE'S NO WI-FI, KEEP THEM ENTERTAINED WITH THE MOST HEE-LARIOUS JOKES ON THE PLANET. IT'S TRUE!

CHAPTER 1
IN THE KITCHEN

11

WHAT DID THE CANNIBAL ORDER AT THE RESTAURANT?
PIZZA WITH EVERYONE ON IT.

DID YOU HEAR ABOUT THE HILARIOUS BANANA?
IT HAD THE WHOLE FRUIT BOWL IN PEELS OF LAUGHTER!

HOW DO YOU MAKE A WALNUT LAUGH?
CRACK IT UP!

WHAT DO YOU GET IF YOU CROSS A SNAKE AND AN APPLE TART?
A PIE-THON!

WHICH DAY OF THE WEEK DO EGGS HATE? FRY-DAY!

HOW DO YOU MAKE AN EGG LAUGH?

TELL IT A YOLK!

BUT WHY SHOULDN'T YOU TELL JOKES TO EGGS?

BECAUSE THEY MIGHT CRACK UP!

DID YOU HEAR ABOUT THE EGG THAT LOVED TO PLAY TRICKS?

IT WAS A PRACTICAL YOLKER!

WAITER, THERE'S A DEAD FLY IN MY SOUP!
SORRY, ARE YOU A VEGETARIAN?

WAITER, THERE'S A TWIG IN MY MEAL!
JUST A MOMENT, I'LL GET THE BRANCH MANAGER.

WAITER, THERE'S AN ANT IN MY SOUP!
I KNOW ... THE FLIES STAY AWAY DURING THE WINTER.

WAITER, WHY IS THERE FISH ON MY PLATE OF LASAGNE?
I'M SORRY, SIR, IT DOESN'T KNOW IT'S PLAICE.

19

WHAT DO YOU CALL SPAGHETTI IN DISGUISE?

AN IMPASTA!

WHAT DO YOU CALL A PEANUT IN SPACE?

AN ASTRONUT!

WHAT'S THE DIFFERENCE BETWEEN ROAST CHICKEN AND PEA SOUP?

ANYONE CAN ROAST CHICKEN, BUT HAVE YOU EVER TRIED TO PEE SOUP?

WHY DID THE CHEF DREAM HIS PILLOW WAS ROAST TURKEY?

BECAUSE THEY'RE BOTH FULL OF STUFFING!

WHAT DO DOGS EAT AT THE MOVIES? PUPCORN!

WHY DID THE TURKEY JOIN A BAND?

HE HAD HIS OWN DRUMSTICKS!

A CHEESEBURGER WALKS INTO A BAR AND ASKS FOR ORANGE JUICE.

THE BARTENDER SAYS, ""I'M SORRY, WE DON'T SERVE FOOD HERE."

WHY DID THE GIRL STARE AT THE CARTON OF JUICE?

BECAUSE IT SAID CONCENTRATE.

WHERE DO TOMATOES HANG OUT ON SUNDAY?

THE SALAD BAR!

WHAT KIND OF ICE CREAM DO BIRDS LIKE THE MOST?

CHOCOLATE CHIRRUP!

DID YOU HEAR ABOUT THE CANNIBAL WEDDING?

THEY TOASTED THE BRIDE AND GROOM!

WHAT'S RED AND DANGEROUS?

SHARK-INFESTED TOMATO SOUP!

WHY COULDN'T THE TEDDY BEAR FINISH ITS LUNCH?

BECAUSE IT WAS STUFFED!

WHY DID THE WALNUT GO OUT WITH A RAISIN?

IT COULDN'T FIND A DATE!

WHAT KIND OF CHEESE DO YOU USE TO LURE A BEAR AWAY?

CAMEMBERT! ("COME ON BEAR!")

WHAT'S THE DIFFERENCE BETWEEN AN ELEPHANT AND A GRAPE?

A GRAPE SQUASHES IF YOU SIT ON IT!

WHAT DID THE SPIDER ORDER AT THE FAST FOOD RESTAURANT?

A BURGER AND FLIES!

SHAKESPEARE WALKED INTO A DINER AND ASKED FOR A DRINK.

THE MAN BEHIND THE COUNTER SHOOK HIS HEAD. "YOU'RE BARD!"

WHY DID THE BOY GIVE MUSTARD TO HIS DOG WHEN IT HAD A FEVER?

IT WAS A HOT DOG!

WHAT DID THE EGG SAY TO THE WHISK?

"I KNOW WHEN I'M BEATEN!"

WHICH DRINK DO SOCCER PLAYERS PLAYER HATE?
PENAL-TEA!

WHY ARE MOST HERBS GOOD AT KEEPING A SECRET?
ONLY THYME WILL TELL!

MOTHER: JIM, HOW MANY MORE TIMES DO I HAVE TO TELL YOU TO WALK AWAY FROM THE COOKIE JAR?
JIM: NONE, I'VE EATEN THEM ALL NOW!

WHAT DO COMPUTER EXPERTS SNACK ON?
MICROCHIPS!

WHY DID THE SAUSAGE ROLL?

BECAUSE IT SAW THE MILKSHAKE!

ARE CARROTS REALLY GOOD FOR YOUR EYESIGHT?

WELL, HAVE YOU EVER SEEN A RABBIT WEARING GLASSES?

WHERE DID THE SPAGHETTI GO TO DANCE?

TO A MEATBALL!

WHAT DID THE CAVEMAN CHOOSE FROM THE MENU?

A CLUB SANDWICH!

43

WHY DO DINOSAURS EAT RAW MEAT?

THEY DON'T KNOW HOW TO COOK!

WHAT CAN A WHOLE APPLE DO THAT HALF AN APPLE CAN'T DO?

IT CAN LOOK ROUND.

WHICH SALAD IS THE BEST AT PLAYING POOL?

THE CUE-CUMBER!

WHAT DO FIREFIGHTERS EAT WITH THEIR CHEESE?

FIRECRACKERS!

45

CHAPTER 2
GET WELL SOON

WHY DID THE CLOWN CALL EMERGENCY SERVICES?

HE BROKE HIS FUNNY BONE!

DOCTOR, IT HURTS WHEN I GO TO THE BATHROOM.

URINE TROUBLE.

DOCTOR, I HAVE NO ENERGY. I CAN'T EVEN WALK DOWN THE ROAD WITHOUT GETTING TIRED.

IT'S BECAUSE YOU'RE WEARING LOAFERS!

WHY DID THE VAN BOUNCE DOWN THE ROAD?

IT WAS A HICCUP TRUCK!

WHAT DID THE DOCTOR PACK FOR HER TRIP TO THE DESERT?

A THIRST-AID KIT!

DOCTOR, THERE'S A MAN WHO URGENTLY NEEDS YOU TO TREAT SCRATCHES ALL OVER HIS BODY.

WHAT'S HIS NAME?

CLAUDE!

DID YOU HEAR ABOUT THE MAN THAT WAS HIT ON THE HEAD BY AN ICICLE?

IT KNOCKED HIM COLD!

WHAT DID THE DOCTOR SAY TO THE VOLCANO?

"YOU NEED TO QUIT SMOKING!"

WHEN DOES A DOCTOR GET ANGRY?
WHEN SHE RUNS OUT OF PATIENTS!

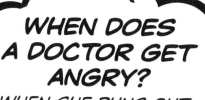

WHY ARE THE TONSILS EXCITED?
THEY'VE HEARD THE DOCTOR IS TAKING THEM OUT ON FRIDAY!

DOCTOR, I KEEP HEARING A RINGING SOUND!
THEN ANSWER YOUR PHONE, DUMMY.

DID YOU HEAR THE JOKE ABOUT THE GERMS?
DON'T WORRY, I DON'T WANT YOU TO SPREAD IT AROUND!

63

WHAT NOISE DID THE TRAIN MAKE WHEN IT HAD A COLD?

AAAA-CHOO-CHOO!

WHY DID THE TRAIN WORKER GET AN ELECTRIC SHOCK?

HE WAS THE CONDUCTOR!

IF AN ATHLETE SUFFERS FROM ATHLETE'S FOOT, WHAT DOES A SOLDIER SUFFER FROM?

MISSILE-TOE!

WHY DID THE HANDYMAN SEE A PSYCHIATRIST?

HE HAD A SCREW LOOSE!

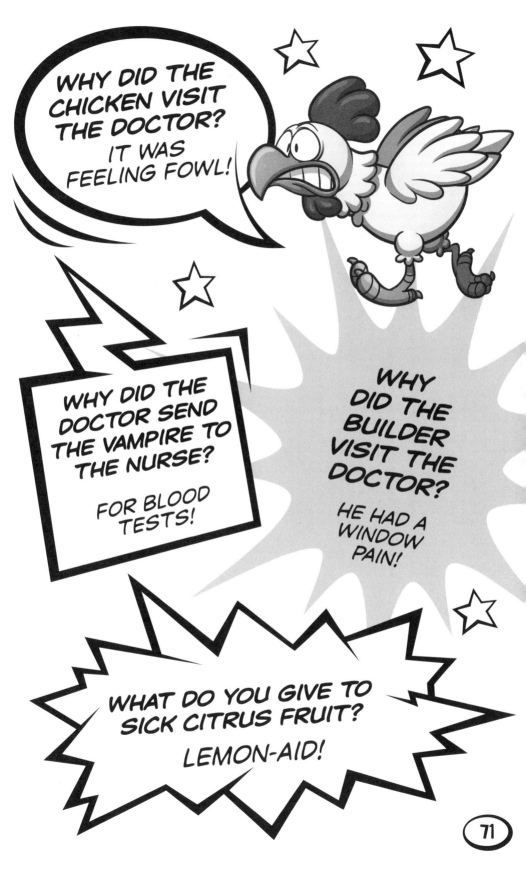

WHY DID THE PONY VISIT THE DOCTOR?

IT WAS A LITTLE HOARSE!

WHAT DID THE DOCTOR PRESCRIBE FOR THE PONY?

COUGH STIRRUP!

THE PONY'S COUGH GOT WORSE. WHAT HAPPENED NEXT?

IT WAS TAKEN TO THE HORSE-PITAL!

HORSE: DOCTOR, I SLEEP ALL DAY AND I'M AWAKE ALL NIGHT.

DOCTOR: YOU'RE A NIGHTMARE!

73

74

75

WHAT DID THE DOCTOR SAY WAS WRONG WITH THE CAR MECHANIC?

HE'D HAD A BREAKDOWN!

THE MECHANIC ASKED FOR A SECOND OPINION.

"HMM," SAID THE DOCTOR. "YOU'RE OVERTIRED."

THE CAR MECHANIC TOLD HIS WIFE WHAT THE DOCTOR SAID.

"YES," SHE AGREED. "YOU DO SEEM EXHAUSTED."

DOCTOR, I KEEP THINKING I'M A BRIDGE!

WHAT'S COME OVER YOU? A LARGE BUS AND SIX CARS!

WHEN SHOULD YOU GO TO SEE A BIRD DOCTOR?

WHEN YOU'RE A PUFFIN!

WHAT DO ELEPHANTS TAKE TO HELP THEM SLEEP?

TRUNKQUILIZERS!

WHY DID THE MUMMY THINK IT HAD A COLD?

BECAUSE OF ITS COFFIN!

DID YOU HEAR ABOUT THE BEAR THAT ENDED UP IN A HOSPITAL?

IT HAD A GRIZZLY ACCIDENT!

83

CHAPTER 3

ON THE FARM

WHAT DID THE VET SAY TO THE GOAT FARMER?
"HOW ARE THE KIDS?"

HOW DO YOU MAKE ANTIFREEZE?
LOCK HER IN THE BARN OVERNIGHT.

HOW DOES A PERUVIAN FARMER WAKE UP IN THE MORNING?
WITH A LLAMA-CLOCK!

FARMER: HOW DO YOU HIRE AN EXTRA WORKER?
FARMER'S SON: SEND HIM UP A LADDER?

WHICH DOG IS THE FASTEST OVER SHORT DISTANCES?

A DASH-HOUND!

WHY DO DOGS RUN IN CIRCLES?

BECAUSE IT'S EASIER THAN RUNNING IN TRIANGLES!

WHAT'S THE MOST USED BUTTON ON A DOG'S TV REMOTE?

PAWS!

WHAT DID THE GUARD DOG SAY WHEN IT FOUND SANDPAPER IN ITS BED?

"RUFF!"

WHICH SPORT DO HORSES PLAY?

STABLE TENNIS!

DID YOU HEAR ABOUT THE PONY THAT RAN AROUND THE WORLD?

IT WAS A GLOBETROTTER!

WHAT DID THE FARMER SAY WHEN HIS HORSE LAY DOWN?

"GIDDY-UP!"

HOW LONG SHOULD A HORSE'S LEGS BE?

LONG ENOUGH TO REACH THE GROUND!

WHAT DID THE GRUB SAY WHEN ITS FRIEND GOT STUCK IN AN APPLE?

"WORM YOUR WAY OUT OF THAT ONE!"

HOW DO DAIRY FARMERS HELP EACH OTHER?

THEY COW-OPERATE!

WHAT HAS 3 HEADS, 2 ARMS, 2 TAILS, AND 8 LEGS?

A FARMER ON HIS HORSE WITH A CHICKEN UNDER HIS ARM!

WHAT DID THE CLEAN DOG SAY TO THE DIRTY DOG?

"LONG TIME, NO FLEA!"

109

WHY DID THE DOG SIT IN THE SHADE? IT DIDN'T WANT TO BE A HOT DOG!

WHY DON'T DOGS TRAVEL BY PLANE? BECAUSE THEY GET JET WAG!

WHY DID THE DOG JUMP IN THE POND? IT SAW A CATFISH!

WHAT DO YOU CALL A SHEEPDOG IN A COUNTRY MEADOW? A COLLIE-FLOWER!

DID YOU HEAR ABOUT THE BEEKEEPER WITH STICKY HAIR?

HE USED A HONEY COMB!

WHAT DID THE BEES DO WHEN THEY MOVED TO A NEW HIVE?

THEY HAD A HOUSE-SWARMING PARTY!

WHAT DO YOU CALL A BEE AND A HORSE THAT LIVE NEAR EACH OTHER?

NEIGH BUZZ!

DID YOU HEAR ABOUT THE BEE THAT MOANED INSTEAD OF BUZZED?

IT WAS A GRUMBLEBEE!

117

119

WHY DO RABBITS HAVE FUR COATS?

BECAUSE THEY'D LOOK RIDICULOUS IN LEATHER JACKETS!

WHAT DO YOU CALL A RABBIT IN A BAKERY?

A STICKY BUNNY!

DID YOU HEAR ABOUT THE RABBIT THAT STOLE THE FARMER'S CARROTS AND THEN RAN AWAY?

IT ESCAPED TO THE HAREPORT!

WHY DID THE TWO RABBITS VISIT A NEW FARM?

THEY WERE ON THEIR BUNNYMOON!

WHAT DO SCARECROWS LIKE TO EAT?

STRAW-BERRIES!

WHY DID THE SCARECROW WIN A PRIZE?

BECAUSE HE WAS OUTSTANDING IN HIS FIELD!

WHY DID THE SCARECROW WANT TO STAND IN A CORNFIELD?

BECAUSE IT WAS A-MAIZE-ING!

WHY DON'T SCARECROWS NEED FEEDING?

BECAUSE THEY'RE ALREADY STUFFED!

CHAPTER 4
AT SCHOOL

BEN: WHEN I GROW UP, I WANT TO BE A SCHOOL BUS DRIVER.

TEACHER: WELL, I WON'T STAND IN YOUR WAY!

WHAT KIND OF BUS TAKES YOU THROUGH SCHOOL, NOT TO SCHOOL?

A SYLLABUS!

WHAT DO YOU SAY IF YOUR ENGLISH TEACHER IS CRYING?

"THERE, THEIR, THEY'RE."

WHERE DO VAMPIRE TEACHERS COME FROM?

TEACHER DRAINING SCHOOL!

TEACHER: HAVE YOU PUT CLEAN WATER IN THE FISH TANK?

STEVE: NO, IT HASN'T DRUNK THE FIRST TANKFUL YET.

TEACHER: DIDN'T I TELL YOU TO STAND AT THE END OF THE QUEUE?

JAMIE: I TRIED, BUT THERE WAS SOMEBODY THERE ALREADY!

WHY DID THE BOY EAT HIS HOMEWORK?

HIS TEACHER SAID IT WAS A PIECE OF CAKE!

WHICH COUNTRY DO GEOGRAPHY TEACHERS LIKE BEST?

EXPLA-NATION!

WHAT HAPPENED WHEN THE BABY WENT TO SCHOOL?
THERE WAS A CRY-SIS!

WHAT KIND OF TEACHER ENJOYS REGISTRATION?
ONE THAT IS ABSENT-MINDED!

TEACHER: WHICH WAS THE FIRST ANIMAL IN SPACE?
EMMA: THE COW THAT JUMPED OVER THE MOON?

WHAT'S BLACK AND WHITE AND HARD?
A PHYSICS TEST!

WHICH TOILET PAPER DO MATHEMATICS TEACHERS PREFER?

MULTI-PLY!

WHY DID THE GEOMETRY TEACHER STAY AT HOME?

SHE HAD SPRAINED HER ANGLE!

WHY DID THE SCIENCE TEACHER WEAR SUNGLASSES?

BECAUSE HIS CLASS WAS SO BRIGHT!

TEACHER: IF I HAD 6 APPLES IN ONE HAND AND 8 APPLES IN THE OTHER, WHAT WOULD I HAVE?

SALLY: ENORMOUS HANDS, SIR!

WHY IS THERE LIGHTNING IN THE STAFF ROOM? THE TEACHERS ARE BRAINSTORMING!

TEACHER: PETER, I HOPE I DIDN'T SEE YOU LOOKING AT RYAN'S EXAM PAPER? PETER: I HOPE YOU DIDN'T, EITHER!

ELLA: WHAT KIND OF CREATURE IS THAT? TEACHER: IT'S OUR PET, TINY. ELLA: BUT WHAT ANIMAL IS IT? TEACHER: IT'S MY-NEWT!

DAD: WHY ARE YOUR HISTORY GRADES SO LOW? EMILY: THEY KEEP ASKING ABOUT THINGS THAT HAPPENED BEFORE I WAS BORN!

147

153

155

WHAT DID THE MOTHER HURRICANE SAY TO HER SON?
"I'VE GOT MY EYE ON YOU!"

GEOGRAPHY TEACHER: HOW DO YOU CUT THE OCEAN IN HALF?

SALLY: WITH A SEA SAW, SIR!

WHAT KIND OF HAIR DOES A MARINE BIOLOGIST HAVE?

WAVY!

WHAT DID THE BOY SAY WHEN HE SAW SOME RAINDROPS ON THE WINDOW?
"TWO'S COMPANY, THREE'S A CLOUD!"

SORRY I'M LATE, TEACHER, I OVERSLEPT.

WHAT, YOU MEAN YOU SLEEP AT HOME AS WELL?

OUR TEACHER TALKS TO HERSELF.

SO DOES OURS, BUT SHE THINKS WE'RE LISTENING!

DAD: HOW DID YOUR EXAMS GO?

HARVEY: I ALMOST GOT IN THE TOP 10 IN EVERY SUBJECT! WELL—I GOT ZERO EACH TIME.

TEACHER: I'D LIKE TO GO THROUGH A WHOLE LESSON WITHOUT TELLING YOU OFF.

SAM: BE MY GUEST.

WHAT DO YOU GET WHEN YOU DIVIDE THE CIRCUMFERENCE OF A JACK-O'-LANTERN BY ITS DIAMETER?

PUMPKIN PI!

WHAT'S THE DEFINITION OF ASYMMETRY?

A PLACE WHERE YOU BURY DEAD MATHEMATICS TEACHERS!

TEACHER: MICHELLE, ARE THOSE NEW GLASSES?

MICHELLE: YES, I'M HOPING THEY'LL IMPROVE DI-VISION!

TEACHER: SEVEN IS AN ODD NUMBER, BUT HOW DO YOU MAKE IT EVEN?

STACEY: TAKE AWAY THE "S"!

LOOPY LIBRARY

LEARNING A LOT
BY I. WANDA KNOW

TEACH YOURSELF WOODWORK
BY HOWARD U. DOOIT

DON'T ANSWER BACK
BY XAVIER BREATH

FOSSIL FUELS
BY M. T. TANK

TRICEPS AND DELTOIDS
BY ARMAND SHOULDER

THE CLASS CHEF
BY IKE N. COOK

TROPICAL DISEASES
BY IVAN ITCH

MAKING PEOPLE JUMP
BY OLIVER SUDDEN

HOW TO COME FIRST
BY VIC TROY

ARITHMETIC
BY ADAM UPMAN

CHAPTER 5

WILD ANIMALS

175

WHAT DID THE LION SAY WHEN THE ZOOKEEPER STOPPED IT FROM EATING A FAMOUS POET?

"YOU TOOK THE WORDS RIGHT OUT OF MY MOUTH!"

WHAT HAPPENED TO THE LION THAT SPENT CHRISTMAS AT THE BEACH?

IT GOT SANDY CLAWS!

WHY WOULDN'T THE HYENA PLAY CARDS WITH THE OTHER ANIMALS?

BECAUSE ONE WAS A CHEETAH, AND THE OTHER WAS LION!

WHY DID THE LION EAT THE TIGHTROPE WALKER?

IT WANTED A WELL-BALANCED MEAL!

WHAT'S BROWN AND DANGEROUS AND LIVES IN A TREE?
A MONKEY WITH A HAND GRENADE!

WHAT'S LARGE AND SQUIRTS JAM AT YOU?
AN ELEPHANT EATING A DONUT!

DID YOU HEAR ABOUT THE SNAKE THAT SWALLOWED SOME KEYS?

IT GOT LOCKJAW!

WHAT DO YOU CALL AN ALLIGATOR THAT WORKS FOR THE POLICE?
AN INVESTI-GATOR!

191

195

197

WHERE DO VAMPIRE FISH LIVE?

IN THE BLOOD STREAM!

WHAT'S THE MOST COMMON MUSIC IN THE JUNGLE?

SNAKE, RATTLE, AND ROLL!

WHAT DID THE INSECT SAY BEFORE IT TRIED BUNGEE JUMPING?

EARWIG-O!

LITTLE SNAKE: DAD, ARE WE POISONOUS?

DAD: NO, HONEY, WHY?

LITTLE SNAKE: I JUST BIT MY LIP!

WHAT DO YOU CALL A FLYING SKUNK?

A SMELLYCOPTER!

WHAT'S YELLOW AND BLACK WITH RED SPOTS?

A LEOPARD WITH MEASLES!

WHAT DO YOU GET IF YOU CROSS A SNAKE AND A PIG?

A BOAR CONSTRICTOR!

WHAT GOES GRRR, SQUELCH, GRRR, SQUELCH?

A LION IN SOGGY SHOES!

WHY DIDN'T THE PENGUIN GET MARRIED?

BECAUSE IT GOT COLD FEET!

WHY DO PENGUINS CARRY FISH IN THEIR BEAK?

BECAUSE THEY DON'T HAVE ANY POCKETS!

HOW DOES A PENGUIN TRAVEL ACROSS THE ICE?

IT JUST GOES WITH THE FLOE!

WHAT DO YOU CALL TWO MATCHING PENGUINS?

PENG-TWINS!

WHICH OF JACK SPARROW'S COUSINS LIVE IN THE JUNGLE?

THE PARROTS OF THE CARIBBEAN!

WHAT BIRDS ARE USELESS AT CROSS COUNTRY RUNNING?

PUFFINS!

WHERE DO BIRDS GO IN THE EVENINGS?

TO A CROWBAR!

WHAT TYPE OF FISH DO BIRDS LIKE BEST?

PERCH!

WHAT DID THE WHALE DO WHEN IT WATCHED A WEEPY MOVIE?

STARTED TO BLUBBER!

WHAT'S GREEN AND SLIMY AND FOUND IN THE OCEAN?

WHALE SNOT!

HOW DO YOU MAKE A JELLYFISH LAUGH?

WITH TEN-TICKLES!

WHAT'S LONG AND SLIMY AND LOVES TO DANCE?

A CONGA EEL!

HOW DO MUMMIES HIDE?

THEY WEAR MASKING TAPE!

WHY CAN YOU TRUST A MUMMY WITH YOUR SECRETS?

THEY'RE GOOD AT KEEPING THINGS UNDER WRAPS!

WHAT DO YOU CALL A FRIENDLY PHARAOH?

A CHUMMY MUMMY!

WHAT DO EGYPTIAN MONSTERS CALL THEIR PARENTS?

MUMMY AND DEADY!

WHAT DOES A MONSTER TAKE FOR A SPLITTING HEADACHE?

SUPERGLUE!

WHAT'S BIG AND UGLY AND BLUE?
A MONSTER HOLDING ITS BREATH!

HOW DO GHOSTS BEGIN BUSINESS LETTERS?

"TOMB IT MAY CONCERN ..."

WHICH MONSTER IS GOOD AT SCIENCE?
FRANK EINSTEIN!

WHICH GAME DO ZOMBIES LIKE BEST?

CHASE!

WHO DID THE ZOMBIE INVITE TO HIS PARTY?

ANYONE HE COULD DIG UP!

WHAT KIND OF MUSIC DO MUMMYS ENJOY?

WRAP MUSIC!

WHEN IS IT EASY TO BEAT A ZOMBIE IN AN ARGUMENT?

WHEN IT HAS NO LEG TO STAND ON!

WHAT'S A ZOMBIE'S HAPPY HOUR?

ATE O'CLOCK!

WHO WON THE ZOMBIE SPRINT?

NO ONE, IT WAS A DEAD HEAT!

WHAT DOES A ZOMBIE READ FIRST IN THE NEWSPAPER?

ITS HORRORSCOPE!

HOW DO YOU GET INTO A HAUNTED HOUSE?
WITH A SKELETON KEY!
WHAT DOES A HEADLESS HORSEMAN RIDE?
A NIGHTMARE!
WHAT IS WILLIAM SHAKESPOOK'S MOST FAMOUS PLAY?
ROMEO AND GHOULIET!
WHY WAS THE TOWN HALL HAUNTED?
BECAUSE IT HAD A NIGHT-MAYOR!

DID YOU HEAR ABOUT THE WITCH WHO TURNED GREEN?

SHE GOT BROOM SICK ON LONG JOURNEYS!

HOW HIGH DO WITCHES FLY?

WAY UP IN THE ATMOSFEAR!

WHY DID THE WITCH THROW AWAY HER DICTIONARY?

BECAUSE SHE WAS GOOD AT SPELLING!

WHERE DO WITCHES KEEP THEIR KEYS AND PHONE?

IN THEIR HAG BAG!

WHAT DOES A MONSTER GIVE HER HUSBAND ON VALENTINE'S DAY?

UGHS AND KISSES!

WHY SHOULD YOU NEVER LIE TO A MONSTER WITH X-RAY VISION?

BECAUSE IT CAN SEE RIGHT THROUGH YOU!

HOW DO YOU KEEP AN UGLY MONSTER IN SUSPENSE?

I'LL TELL YOU TOMORROW!

WHAT DID THE CRAZY MONSTER PUT ITS LUGGAGE IN?

A HEAD-CASE!

LOOPY LIBRARY

TRACKING UFOS
BY LUKE OUT

SPOTTING A SHOOTING STAR
BY OMAR GOSH

TOP 10 TELESCOPES
BY SEYMOUR STARS

ASTROPHYSICS
BY JEAN YUSS

THE ALIENS ARE HERE!
BY SUE PRIZE

THE EDGE OF THE UNIVERSE
BY OTTO SIGHT

ROCKET LAUNCH
BY IVANA BLASTOV

ALIEN ABDUCTION
BY Y. ME

IS THERE LIFE ON MARS?
BY ESAU WATERS

STARGAZING
BY N. TRANCED